The Golden Compass

FOR CHARACTER-BASED DECISION MAKING

**A skill
for students
and educators**

David B. Wangaard, Ed.D.
The School for Ethical Education

ETHICS IN ACTION CREATES CHARACTER

The Golden Compass for Character-Based Decision Making:
A Skill for Students and Educators

Publisher: Character Development Group, Inc.
P.O. Box 35136, Greensboro, NC 27425-5136
336-668-9373, Fax: 336-668-9375
E-mail: Info@CharacterEducation.com, www.CharacterEducation.com

Layout by Sara Sanders, SHS Design

ISBN-13: 978-1-892056-47-4
$16.95
ISBN-10: 1-892056-47-X
Library of Congress Control Number: 2006939413
Printed in the United States of America

Acknowledgements

Even the smallest of published products can require the support of many individuals and organizations. I am grateful for the support of Wright Investors' Service in Milford, Conn. for their unwavering commitment to The School for Ethical Education. It has also been a privilege to experience the professional encouragement of colleagues such as Kristie Fink, Janice Stoodley, Ann Kenyon and Phil Vincent in the review and editing of this workbook. This text is dedicated to the teachers and students who choose to take the extra step to think dilemmas through ethically. Keep those ethics in action!

Dear Teachers,

Make a good choice! This statement is meant to encourage the hearer to make a good decision. Making good choices that demonstrate positive character requires excellent decision-making skill. Without ever having been taught clear skills for decision making, many of our students lack the background and experience to adequately solve some of their dilemmas.

Merriam-Webster defines dilemma as, "a problem involving a difficult choice."[1] The skills presented in this activity book provide students a *Golden Compass* to help them solve their dilemmas using character-based decision making.

With the *Golden Compass*, positive character provides the needle that always points us in a constructive direction. To master the *Golden Compass*, students need time to understand and practice the four steps in the model. More than 50 practice exercises are provided in this activity book in the form of story dilemmas.

This workbook is written for teachers and includes photocopy activity pages for students in grades 5 to 12. The text is divided into four sections that include:

1. Introduction and rationale for character-based decision making (pages 1-3)
2. Teacher notes and activities to prepare students for use of the *Golden Compass* (pages 5-30)
3. Story dilemmas for students to practice the skill of decision making with relevant school, community and home scenarios (pages 31-89)
4. Resources for extension and evaluation activities (pages 91-98).

I welcome your feedback as you practice the application of the *Golden Compass* with your students. Take time to celebrate any progress you observe in students demonstrating choices for positive character.

David B. Wangaard, Ed.D.
The School for Ethical Education
www.ethicsed.org

---

1. Merriam-Webster Online—http://www.m-w.com/

Table of Contents

Introduction

This activity book is designed to introduce you and your students to the steps that support character-based decision making.

You may choose to jump ahead to the *Golden Compass* model on page 24 and the subsequent dilemmas; however, teaching students the following topics will improve their ability to use character-based decision making. Workbook topics include:

1. **Visualizing Character** (page 5)
2. Establishing **Personal Character Goals** (page 7)
3. **Defining the Golden Mean of Character** (Aristotle's Golden Mean) (page 9)
4. Understanding **Moral Stage Bumping** (Kohlberg's model) (page 12)
5. Practicing **Higher-Order Thinking** (Bloom's Taxonomy) (page 15)
6. Applying the **Golden Rule** (page 22)
7. **Recognizing and Managing Emotions** (page 26)

Each of these topics is designed to provide you and your students with skills and/or information to make the best application of the *Golden Compass*. The activities in this workbook are suggested for use in homeroom settings, class meetings, advisory/advisee periods within discipline plans, health-education classes and language arts or social studies classes that will include the study of decisions by characters in literature or history.

Excellent decision making is an important skill that supports successful living and a positive school environment. The dilemma stories provided in this activity book will provide decision-making practice and discussion material for circumstances that students face at school, home or in their community.

Let us consider one example of a student with a dilemma at school.

Michael is a nice kid with above average potential. He enjoys PE and athletics more than academics. His parents have recently increased their attention to his grades and have threatened loss of some privileges if Michael's grades do not improve. On an errand to the school office, Michael happens to notice copies of his next history test on an office counter. No one is looking at him. He could take one copy and not be noticed.

Clearly Michael is faced with a decision—a dilemma. It could help Michael to remember, "Make a good choice!" It may trigger some obligation to honor his parents by not being caught with a stolen test; however, he may feel a more immediate pressure to improve his grades and believe that stealing the test would be a good choice to help him study. We will look at this case in more detail after the *Golden Compass* character-based decision-making model is introduced.

What is character-based decision making? Students and adults are confronted with choices everyday. Our values, family training, school rules, emotions, and/or self-interest will sometimes guide us. Among the many benefits of schools involved in character education is the recognition that universal values defined by positive character can help guide our choices. Universal values are typically identified to include respect, responsibility, honesty, and caring. If you add the principle of the Golden Rule (do unto others...) you have a powerful reasoning device for character-based decision making as a *Golden Compass*.

The *Golden Compass* is a life skill that can become a profoundly useful tool for students. It has ancient roots in the teaching of Aristotle and avoids some of the ethical difficulties associated with a focus solely on rules (Kantian ethics), maximization of benefits (Utilitarian ethics), selfish goals (Egoist ethics), or subjective relativism where no one can objectively judge a good decision.

It is important to define and understand character before we introduce the *Golden Compass*. Positive character is not difficult to define. Students of all ages are capable of identifying positive and negative character as observed in the behavior of others. Our character simply defined is the sum of our behaviors over time with particular attention to how we act when we are under social or emotional pressure.

If a student is repeatedly observed to take time to help others in need of assistance, one might label their character as kind or empathic. If a student is regularly involved in arguments and disagreements with peers and adults over fine points of games and class administration, one might label their character as contentious. And yes, I can hear some colleagues label this behavior as leadership, but a leader can also learn the art of respectful confrontation and the wisdom of when to make a point. Without wisdom or respect, an argumentative person can be recognized as a difficult person with whom to work.

While this activity book will not attempt to address the psychology behind character development, there are several assumptions made to support the application of the *Golden Compass*. These assumptions include:

- character is demonstrated through behavior,
- character is not locked by genetics into an inflexible temperament or personality,

- character is strongly influenced by culture, environment and education, but is ultimately the result of choices and decisions made by the individual,
- teachers can help students cultivate their power of choice and decision making to demonstrate positive character.

The goal of this activity book is to provide teachers and students a clear outline and opportunity to practice the application of character-based decision making.

The outcomes that can result as students practice the exercises in this activity book include:

- students recognize and understand the steps of how to make a good decision as outlined by the *Golden Compass* strategy,
- students apply and demonstrate positive character as a result of good choices selected during role modeling,
- students are able to analyze and evaluate dilemmas using higher-order thinking skills,
- students demonstrate positive character as a result of decisions made independent of adult supervision while applying the steps of the *Golden Compass*, and
- students can gain more autonomy as they demonstrate positive character.

The desire to make a good choice is recognized to belong in the heart of the individual as he/she relates to others. While this activity book helps to develop cognitive (head) ability and behavioral (hand) ability, I leave to you teachers the responsibility to cultivate the affective (heart) desire in your students to make good choices. The heart to make a good choice is cultivated in students that recognize they are respected and belong to a group that wants to learn and work in a caring and responsible classroom. Publishers such as the Character Development Group[2] and the Northeast Foundation for Children[3] provide excellent resources to help create caring classrooms.

The following activities are provided to introduce you and your students to strategies that support the use of The *Golden Compass*. Now it's your choice! Complete the activities or jump to the dilemmas? What will you choose?

2. Character Development Group, (888) 262-0572, http://www.charactereducation.com/
3. Northeast Foundation for Children, (800) 360-6332, http://www.responsiveclassroom.org/

Teacher Notes and Activities

Visualizing Character

Behaviors that define our personal character can be influenced by many factors. While the reasons some people choose to demonstrate good character and others choose to demonstrate weak character is acknowledged to be complicated; there really should be no mystery about how good and weak character are defined. Students can help us discover clear definitions of good character, and in the process, help us visualize a classroom that would be a great place to work and learn.

The following activity can help establish positive expectations in your classroom and begin a vocabulary list of positive character traits for later application in the *Golden Compass*.

Lesson Activity

Objective: Students will recognize how character can be defined by routine behavior.

Discussion: Introduce your students to the idea of using the term "character" to define behavior in school. Character that supports students' experiencing a successful year can be defined as *helpful* or *positive character*. Using the following statements, lead a class discussion and obtain student feedback on what they define as helpful character. You or a student recorder should write notes on the board or a flip chart regarding student responses for review at the end of the discussion. Reproduce a blank form (as shown on the next page) to capture your notes.

Discussion prompts:

- Describe teacher behaviors that would help everyone experience a successful year.
- Describe student behaviors that would help everyone experience a successful year.
- Label the behaviors you have described with a character trait(s) that is best demonstrated by the helpful behavior.

Notes for Visualizing Character

Record notes from your student discussion on this page or on a flip chart where you reproduce this form.

Behaviors that help create a successful class	Character trait(s) associated with each behavior
Teachers **Example:** Listen to students to understand	Respect
Students **Example:** Come to class prepared	Responsibility

As you complete the exercise, **Visualizing Character**, you will probably find character traits such as respect, caring, cooperation, fairness, good humor, and responsibility on your summary list. Your class will identify a list of positive character traits that if demonstrated in daily behavior, will help everyone reach their full potential and create a successful class environment.

You can build on this exercise to create class expectations, procedures and rules; however, that is a different task than our goal at hand. For more information about the process of connecting character traits to class expectations visit The School for Ethical Education's website at http://www.ethicsed.org/consulting/promote.htm.

Next, we want to personalize this exercise and ask students to identify their own character goals to help them achieve personal success in school and in life.

Personal Character Goals

The worksheet on the next page may be copied for each student to complete individually as homework or during a class session. Their personal character goals will become the magnetic north of a character-based decision-making compass.

After the **Personal Character Goals** worksheet is completed, collect the student responses. As a group exercise, add any new information from the students' personal goals to the list of character goals from the previously completed exercise **Visualizing Character** (page 6).

Save this list of character goals and the definitions for future reference or the possible creation of a class character-expectations poster.

Extension Activity

Have your class summarize the list of **Personal Character Goals** (page 8) and **Visualizing Character Traits** (page 6). The class can complete a ranking exercise by having each student vote for their top three character goals. Tabulate the student voting and identify the top four or five character goals for the class. These goals can become the focus of class expectations and norms. Students could help create a poster of these norms with visual depictions or short definitions of how the character traits are demonstrated at school.

Student Worksheet: Personal Character Goals

Name _____

From the following list of character traits (1) circle three traits (or trait groups) you believe would help you personally experience a successful school year and, (2) in the open spaces that follow define each of your personal character goals by noting specific behaviors that you could demonstrate to accurately represent the traits at school, at home, or in the community.

Some of the traits below have been grouped as they represent similar behaviors. You may delete or add character traits to the group if it helps you define your character goals.

CHARACTER TRAITS			
Caring/Compassion/ Empathy/Kindness	Citizenship/Service	Cheerfulness/Humor	Confidence/Optimism
Cooperation	Courage	Creativity	Dependability/Diligence/ Reliability/Responsibility
Fairness	Honesty/Integrity/ Trustworthiness	Generosity	Initiative/Industry
Leadership	Loyalty	Patience	Perseverance
Respect	Self-control	Tolerance	Other trait(s)

Define your character traits (or character groups) with specific behaviors to create personal goals:

1. *I demonstrate* _____ *when* _____
                 (character trait)   (list specific behaviors)

   _____

   _____

2. *I demonstrate* _____ *when* _____
                 (character trait)   (list specific behaviors)

   _____

   _____

3. *I demonstrate* _____ *when* _____
                 (character trait)   (list specific behaviors)

   _____

   _____

Defining the Golden Mean of Character

Let us take one more step to understand the value of character in defining personal behavior. Aristotle (384-322 BC)[4] is recognized as one of the great contributors to Western thought. He was a teacher in ancient Greece who focused on the value of developing character to live a virtuous and successful life. The Greeks recognized that character traits could be demonstrated in many different ways. Aristotle taught the value of finding the *Golden Mean* of character, which meant living in the balance between deficit and excess of any particular character trait. For example, courage could be a weak character trait as demonstrated in cowardice, or courage could be seen to be in excess if a person became foolhardy.

Lesson Activity (Discussion)

Objective: Students will recognize weak and excessive character to help define the *Golden Mean* of balanced character.

Introduce the concept of the *Golden Mean* of character to your students. Discuss the example of courage in the table here. Have students provide examples of specific behaviors to define courage as weak character, as the *Golden Mean* and in excess. Additional examples can be discussed with the character traits of respect and honesty.

Specific examples to define the Golden Mean of Character

Weak Character	Golden Mean of Character	Excessive Demonstration
Weak Courage—run away from a challenge	**Courage**—standing up for something you believe in	**Excessive Courage**—taking risks of injury or loss for something of low value
Weak Respect—dismissive or insulting to others	**Respect**—listening and considering others' opinions	**Excessive Respect**—deference to others which may be perceived as empty flattery or manipulative
Weak Honesty—cannot be trusted in word or action	**Honesty**—tells the truth with discretion and wisdom	**Excessive Honesty**—tells the truth without discretion and unnecessarily harms others

4. From Wikipedia, source—http://en.wikipedia.org/wiki/Aristotle

Notes for Defining the Golden Mean of Character

Directions: After reviewing the examples on the previous page, use the character traits students selected for their **Personal Character Goals** and assign the students to individually complete the following worksheet **Defining the Golden Mean of Character**. This exercise will help students describe the range of weak to excessive behaviors associated with their character goals and restate clear behaviors that would define their Golden Mean.

Conduct a class discussion to summarize the behaviors students have identified to define weak character, excessive character and the Golden Mean of character for specific character traits. Use the discussion to help form a consensus (not everyone has to agree) about the behavioral definitions for selected character traits.

Discussions that help support consensus building are supported by two principles that include (1) students respect the opinion of others, and (2) students demonstrate reasonableness and ability to compromise over disputes so that the class can make progress together.

These definitions of balanced character are the guiding needle of the *Golden Compass* decision-making model.

Student Worksheet: Defining the Golden Mean of Character

Name _____

Directions: In a class discussion, identify examples for weak character, excessive character and the Golden Mean of character. Use your personal character goals to complete the following table. For each of the character traits you have chosen to demonstrate as a personal goal, identify behaviors that would describe that trait as weak character, the Golden Mean of character and excessive character. Be prepared to discuss your examples with your class.

1. Personal Character Goal_____

Weak Character	Golden Mean of Character	Excessive Demonstration

2. Personal Character Goal_____

Weak Character	Golden Mean of Character	Excessive Demonstration

3. Personal Character Goal_____

Weak Character	Golden Mean of Character	Excessive Demonstration

Behaviors in the Golden Mean create excellent goals for us to live by. We will apply these examples of behavior as we begin to use *The Golden Compass.*

Moral Stage Bumping

Lawrence Kohlberg (1927-1987)[5] spent much of his career in the development of a six-stage model of moral reasoning. Kohlberg's six stages resulted from research that suggested there are developmentally progressive stages of moral reasoning that could be achieved by people who mature from Stage One (focus on self) to Stage Six (focus on universal moral principles). His model encouraged individuals to develop their moral reasoning through the activity of discussing moral dilemmas.

Kohlberg used dilemmas to involve students in discussion to help promote "stage bumping," or the gradual movement of moral reasoning from a lower stage to a higher stage. An adapted outline of his six-stage model is presented here.

The goal for our understanding these stages is to recognize what might define a student's current motivation in moral reasoning. With this knowledge, a teacher can plan appropriate strategies to motivate children to make positive choices. Teachers can also encourage progress in their students' moral reasoning to promote moral stage bumping. For example, a student focused on Stage Two (What's in it for me?) could be provided opportunities to enjoy the satisfaction of serving others through class activities. Reflecting on a successful service activity can help a student "bump" from Stage Two to Stage Three with the resulting increase in the concern for others that will support character-based decision making.

Outline of Kohlberg's Six Moral Stages

Level and Stage	Motives for Choices
Pre-Conventional **Stage One**	I strive to get what I want for personal pleasure while seeking to avoid punishment for any of my behaviors.
Stage Two	I recognize there are rewards for cooperating but focus on "What's in it for me?"
Conventional **Stage Three**	I understand and share the expectations of a small community (family, school, club) and want to please others and apply the Golden Rule with those in close relationship with me.
Stage Four	I see the expectations and needs of the larger society and desire to maintain rules, laws and social conventions to keep civil order.
Post Conventional **Stage Five**	I have a desire to see the greatest good for the greatest number of people. I can argue for values that supersede conventional social norms or rules.
Stage Six	I hold a personal commitment to universal moral principles and can speak up for values of justice which may oppose conventional social norms, rules and the happiness of the majority.

5. http://en.wikipedia.org/wiki/Kohlberg%27s_stages_of_moral_development

Notes for Moral Stage Bumping

Recognizing the moral stage of students as defined by Kohlberg is useful in our work to promote wise decision making. Students that reason with Stage One thinking will not respond to the same motivating factors as those in Stages Three and higher.

A first step to apply Kohlberg's Six-Stage Model (as described on the previous page) is to qualitatively evaluate your class and understand the range of moral reasoning that currently exists in your students. This can be accomplished by simple observation of student behavior over time, or you could use a student questionnaire to capture a snap shot of student moral reasoning.

A student questionnaire (**What Motivates Me**) is provided in the resource section (pages 91-93) and includes its own scoring rubric to estimate your students' moral reasoning stages. With this information, consider strategies to develop your students' moral reasoning ability. You can help them "stage bump" with the goal to have the majority of your class reasoning at Kohlberg's Stage Three or higher. Stage Three is the first stage where students begin to respect the needs of others who are relationally close to them as defined by the Golden Rule—*Do unto others as you would have them do unto you.*

Teacher Activity

Objective: The teacher will become familiar with Kohlberg's six-stages of moral development and identify age-appropriate strategies to increase student moral reasoning.

Directions: Review and compare the stage bumping strategies suggested in the following table with Kohlberg's six-stage model and add two ideas of your own that could be applied in your classroom.

Suggested strategies for Moral Stage Bumping (Stage One to Stage Four)

Student Moral Stage	Stage Bumping Strategy
Stage One	• Make rules and consistently enforce consequences for misbehavior that requires reflection on choices. • Provide appropriate incentives for good choices and behavior with care to advance from extrinsic to intrinsic rewards. • Provide opportunities for successful contribution to group tasks. **Your ideas:**
Stage Two	• Have students participate in goal setting that moves beyond extrinsic rewards for successful completion of tasks. • Engage students in service of others and reflect on outcomes. • Have students reflect on the needs of others through direct experience or through current events or literature. • Students practice application of the *Golden Compass*. **Your ideas:**
Stage Three	• Encourage students' experiences and collaboration with those outside their immediate relationships and reflect on process. • Engage students in reading meaningful stories or literature about different cultures or people groups. • Provide service opportunities and reflection that engage students with different cultures. • Students practice application of the *Golden Compass*. **Your ideas:**
Stage Four	• Encourage students' reflection on the root causes of injustice in society. • Engage students in service learning to address meaningful needs within community and reflect on long-term solutions. • Students practice application of the *Golden Compass*. **Your ideas:**

Higher-Order Thinking

One last teaching strategy is provided here to promote wise decision making. Most state standards make a point of encouraging teachers to develop higher-order thinking skills in their students. A well understood framework for identifying low to high level reasoning skills is Bloom's Taxonomy[6]. As outlined on the following page, Benjamin Bloom created this taxonomy for categorizing levels of abstraction that can be applied to developmentally appropriate instruction. The taxonomy provides a useful structure to categorize instruction. Becoming familiar with the taxonomy can help guide us in the development of lesson plans that promote higher-order reasoning skills. Higher-order reasoning skills are critically important for students to make wise decisions.

Decision making requires students to have competence in the ability to analyze facts (see patterns of cause and effect, and organize information) and form an evaluation (make a determination and assess value). These two competencies are the highest-order categories in Bloom's Taxonomy. Teaching strategies that help students practice these competencies are consistent with good academic goals and support the skills needed for excellent decision making.

Teachers can become important facilitators of ethical lessons using higher-order thinking skills and the vocabulary of character. Applying the definitions of Bloom's competencies to our lesson plans, students learn the richness and depth of meaning for character as they master a *knowledge* of character. *Knowledge* of character will help them list, define and identify character traits. *Comprehension* of these character traits will provide students the ability to describe, contrast and discuss the meaning of character within the stories or history they are studying. The ability to comprehend provides a useful foundation for students to make direct *application* of the lessons associated with character. *Application* skills are defined by the students' ability to demonstrate, illustrate and show how character was manifest in the story or history under study. Students may *synthesize* a new solution to a dilemma as they create their own application. And finally, students can be guided to *analyze* and *evaluate* using their comprehension of character as they read about people in current events, historical events, literature or in the dilemmas they face.

6. Bloom, B.S. (Ed.) (1956) Taxonomy of educational objectives: The classification of educational goals: Handbook I, cognitive domain. New York: Longmans.

Higher-Order Thinking: Bloom's Taxonomy

Levels of competence as described in this adapted version of Bloom's Taxonomy are defined by the skills demonstrated by students and are assumed to progress from the lowest to highest levels of competency in a developmental order. Student mastery of higher-order thinking skills is typically required in state learning standards and is essential to excellent decision making.

Competence	Skills Demonstrated
Knowledge	• observation and recall of definitions of character • knowledge of examples, role models • knowledge of behaviors that demonstrate specific character traits • mastery of subject matter • **Question Cues:** list, define, tell, identify, show, label, collect, quote, name, who, when, where, etc.
Comprehension	• understanding a continuum that defines each character trait • grasp meaning and benefit of positive character • interpret facts • infer causes • predict consequences, understand strategies to develop character • **Question Cues:** summarize, describe, interpret, contrast, predict, associate, distinguish, estimate, differentiate, discuss, extend
Application	• use definitions of positive character in personal and group goal setting • use strategies of character development • translate knowledge character into action • solve problems and conflicts and demonstrate positive character • **Question Cues:** apply, demonstrate, calculate, complete, illustrate, show, solve, relate
Analysis	• seeing patterns of cause and effect related to demonstrated character • organization of facts to support application of character • recognition of hidden meanings • identification of stages to implement character development • **Question Cues:** analyze, separate, order, examine, explain, connect, classify, arrange, divide, compare, summarize
Synthesis	• use old ideas to create new strategies • generalize from given facts • relate knowledge of character from different communities, cultures • predict, draw conclusions • **Question Cues:** combine, integrate, modify, rearrange, change, substitute, plan, create, design, invent, what if?, compose, formulate, prepare, generalize, rewrite, discover
Evaluation	• make determinations and discriminate between choices with different character outcomes • assess value of theories and strategies to promote character • identify choices based on reasoned argument • verify value of evidence • recognize subjectivity • **Question Cues:** assess, decide, rank, grade, test, measure, recommend, select, judge, discriminate, support, conclude

Notes for Higher-Order Thinking

Stories about youth are particularly helpful to provide students the opportunity to practice analysis and evaluation of the decisions by others. Three stories are provided here to support students practicing the development of their thinking skills. These skills will be transferred to the application of the *Golden Compass*, which will reciprocally support further development of higher-order thinking skills as students—

- Seek to **comprehend** dilemmas they face
- Make application of their **knowledge** of character with the *Golden Compass*
- **Analyze** dilemmas to examine possible character outcomes for different choices
- **Synthesize** solutions to generate the best character outcome and demonstrate respect for others
- **Evaluate** potential or actual character outcomes in relation to chosen action steps.

While the skills of different competencies in Bloom's Taxonomy are acknowledged to overlap, there is value in recognizing the concrete skills of knowledge, comprehension and application and the skills requiring more abstract reasoning ability to analyze, synthesize and evaluate. After the mastery of the concrete skills, Bloom suggests that students can learn strategies to analyze information, which allows them to separate, order, explain and classify behaviors they have witnessed or read about in stories or literature. Analysis supports students' ability to synthesize their learning with past experience and knowledge to plan, create, invent and formulate new applications with their skills.

Bloom describes the highest-order competency as that of evaluation. Evaluation takes analysis and makes decisions based on judgments of value, rank or other evidence. Developing the competence of evaluation using a comprehension of character is the objective of every application of the *Golden Compass*. Students practicing evaluation with the story dilemmas that follow will improve their moral reasoning ability.

Analysis, synthesis and evaluation are the reasoning competencies required for mature use of the *Golden Compass*. Students who master these competencies will be able to apply the *Golden Compass* to dilemmas outside of the role-plays and supervised discussions in class into new circumstances they face in and out of school.

The capacity to reason at the higher stages of analysis and evaluation are traditionally thought to require students to reach 12 to 13 years of age. However, authors such as Thomas Lickona[7] and Robert Coles[8] have recognized that students in primary grades can develop these skills and be useful role models to their peers.

7. Lickona, T. (1991). *Educating for Character*. New York: Bantam.

8. Coles, R. (1997). The moral intelligence of children: How to raise a moral child. New York: Random House.

Lesson Activity: Developing Higher-Order Thinking

Objective: Students will be introduced to the competencies of Bloom's taxonomy and respond to story-based prompts to practice higher-order thinking skills.

Directions: In the following three stories, young people have faced challenges or dilemmas and chosen to demonstrate positive character. Discussion questions are included with each story to support the progressive development of reasoning from less complex questions seeking knowledge and comprehension to more abstract questions seeking students to practice synthesis, analysis and evaluation. The three stories are adapted with permission from *My Hero*[9]. *My Hero* maintains their website to publish hero stories of children and adults. *My Hero* invites students to write and add their own stories about people who have demonstrated heroic behavior. Many of the *My Hero* stories highlight people who have made a series of decisions that define great character in action.

Copy the following story worksheets for students to work in pairs or individually. In three different sessions, have the students write notes responding to the story prompts and then lead a class discussion. Allow the students to evaluate the different levels of reasoning required to respond to each of the three prompts. Have the students summarize each discussion and encourage them to make application of their discussion to school or personal life.

Extension Activity

Practice leading student discussions to analyze and evaluate choices with the dilemmas in this activity book, other stories from *My Hero,* relevant stories in your curriculum or current events. The development of higher-order reasoning skills will support your students' application of the *Golden Compass* and all their other reasoning tasks.

9. *My Hero* website—http://myhero.com

Bethany Hamilton: A Choice for Persistence and Optimism

Story Adapted from: *Never Give Up* by Tyler H. from Sycamore Jr. High for MyHero Project[10]

Bethany surfing after the loss of her arm. (Bethany Hamilton Support Website www.bethanyhamilton.com)

On October 31st, 2003, young surfer, Bethany Hamilton suffered a big loss. But it wasn't a loss in one of her many surfing heats, she lost her arm! It was Halloween morning in Hawaii, and it was sunny and a perfect day for surfing. Bethany decided that she would go surfing near Tunnels Beach with her best friend, Alana Blanchard and Alana's father and brother. She was catching great waves and all of a sudden, her life changed in an instant. She was attacked by a 14-foot tiger shark! The shark bit her just 4 inches below her left shoulder and took the rest of her arm off! She was able to compose herself, and swim to safety.

Bethany was planning on being a professional surfer before her accident in the waves. She was ranked 8th in the world for amateur surfers beforehand. She has overcome the loss of her left arm and rose to the challenge of going surfing out in the ocean again.

Her bravery and courage are evident and those are true hero qualities.... She is now a role model to many people for what she has done. She turned a negative into a positive.... She did this by taking the tragedy that occurred and remained positive and continued to go forward with her dream. This has inspired millions of people all across the world to try to find something good in something that only seems bad. She has chosen through her optimism and persistence to keep her surfing career alive.

Knowledge/comprehension: In what way do you believe Bethany has become a role model?

Application/Synthesis: Describe a situation where choosing to be positive and optimistic might help you.

Analysis/Evaluation: How important is persistence to living a successful life? Support your opinion.

10. http://www.myhero.com/myhero/hero.asp?hero=Bethany_SJH_ Written by Tyler H. from Sycamore Jr. High

Student Worksheet

Name _____

Ibrahim Alex Bangura: A Choice for Tolerance and Peace

Story adapted from *Peacemaker* by Wendy Jewell for MyHero Project[11]

Ibrahim Alex Bangura

It seems almost surreal...playing soccer at night, in an African field, lit only by a dizzying array of stars, but that's what Ibrahim Alex Bangura loves to do. He also loves listening to Whitney Houston. He is like any other 16-year-old except for the fact that on November 16, 1999, he was the winner in the Performing Arts category of the Global Youth Peace & Tolerance Awards and the United Nations in New York City. This ceremony honored youth who apply their creative talents to the cause of peace.

Sierra Leone, the poorest country in Africa, has been torn apart by a seven-year civil war. When Alex joined Peace Links at age 10, he immediately demonstrated an ability to identify the causes of the problems facing his country and offer creative ideas for projects. He has helped UNICEF to distribute oral rehydration packets during cholera outbreaks, worked on environmental clean-up projects and built shelters. He has led workshops on tolerance, and educated children about the United Nations' goals for world peace and about the Convention on the Rights of the Child.

Alex's current focus is on the rehabilitation of thousands of children who were kidnapped and trained to be soldiers. They came to believe that life has no meaning. Peace Links teaches these children songs about peace and tolerance in an effort to change their value system and redirect their lives.

Alex's family is poor. He walks long distances to meetings, workshops and concerts when transportation is unavailable. He often goes without meals in order to get to places on time and because food is scarce in Sierra Leone. Yet he always makes sure to finish his many hours of homework. His scholastic record is excellent and he hopes to attend college someday.

Knowledge/comprehension: List the number of projects in which Ibrahim participated. You should be able to find seven if you count separately the different teaching workshops. Are there any projects in your school or community that have similar goals?

Application/Synthesis: Create a voluntary survey of your class and record a brief description of service projects classmates have participated in within the past year.

Analysis/Evaluation: Compare and evaluate a summary of your class' involvement in service to Ibahim's list of service activity.

11. http://www.myhero.com/myhero/hero.asp?hero=Ibrahim, Written by Wendy Jewell, Photos courtesy of Peace Links Sierra Leone

Mory Sanberg: A Choice for Compassion

Story adapted from: *Community Hero* for MyHero Project[12]

Mory (front, far right) with friends making sandwiches in her kitchen.

Mory Sanberg, like many teenagers, was restless, eager to have her freedom, and yet, insecure about who she was and who she wanted to be. And she had a lot of compassion for kids who were "having a hard time" for one reason or another. She decided to focus her community service on helping homeless children and teenagers. She felt this was one place she might be able to make a difference. She contacted several organizations that basically ignored her because she was only 14 years old. The staff at The Night Ministry was different. Everyone embraced her enthusiasm and encouraged her to develop a program that would meet the needs of the homeless.

Mory began to make hundreds of bag dinners each week during the summer, which were distributed by The Night Ministry to homeless teenagers. The meals, which included a sandwich, fruit, chips and cookies, were assembled in Mory's kitchen with support from her parents and friends. Then Mory came up with the idea to give disadvantaged and homeless children holiday stockings filled with goodies. She realized this might be the only gift many of these children would receive during the holidays. Mory raised money, enlisted friends and family, and embarked on a mission to spread holiday cheer to teenagers and children living on the edge.

What started as an assignment from her family and school became a passion for Mory. In the past four summers, she provided over 4,000 bag dinners, and in the last three years, over 1,000 Christmas stockings and gifts to kids. In addition, she has had a wonderful time.

Knowledge/comprehension: Who did Mory help? Did Mory resent or enjoy her service project?

Application/Synthesis: How could you organize a service project that is enjoyable for the participants?

Analysis/Evaluation: How meaningful was Mory's project? Do you think all service has to be fun? Why or why not?

12. http://www.myhero.com/myhero/hero.asp?hero=M_sanberg, written by My Hero

The Golden Rule

Let's review the main ideas that have been introduced to this point.

- Positive character can be described by observable behavior
- Positive character as defined by students applying the Golden Mean describe helpful behaviors for individual or classroom expectations and norms
- Moral reasoning has developmental stages as defined by Lawrence Kohlberg
- Moral reasoning can be increased through discussion of dilemmas
- Reasoning can be strengthened by practicing higher-order thinking skills as described in Bloom's Taxonomy
- Higher-order thinking that applies an understanding of positive character supports students in the analysis and evaluation of dilemmas

Aristotle taught that the virtuous or moral person would define his/her virtue by demonstrating positive character. Lawrence Kohlberg's theory of moral development advanced the concept that moral reasoning can occur as individuals used higher-order thinking skills to resolve dilemmas.

The *Golden Compass* borrows from both traditions to encourage decisions that are reasoned to produce the most satisfactory character outcome. The model also includes reflection on the **law of reciprocity** or the Golden Rule. Throughout history and in all cultures the principle of the Golden Rule has been understood.[13]

What you do not want done to yourself, do not do unto others.

Confucius (500 BC) China

We should behave to others as we wish others to behave to us.

Aristotle (325 BC) Greece

Do nothing to thy neighbor which thou wouldst not have him do to thee thereafter.

Mahabharata (200BC) India

Do unto others, as you would have them do unto you.

Jesus (33AD) Israel

It is not fair to ask of others what you are unwilling to do yourself.

Eleanor Roosevelt (1940s) United States

Notes for the Golden Rule

The Golden Rule is a leveraging principle that immediately encourages us to take the perspective of another person. In respect to Kohlberg's stages of moral reasoning, it forces a person to reason at a minimum of Stage Three and be concerned for how their behavior affects others.

13. Character Counts. (1995). *Train-the-Trainer Manual.* Los Angeles, CA: Josephson Institute of Ethics

Lesson Activity

Objective: Students will understand the principle of the Golden Rule and practice steps to identify who might be affected by their choices.

Directions: Ask the students to state from memory a version of the Golden Rule. Record a consensus version for class application. Compare your version with the historical versions of the Golden Rule noted on the preceding page. Discuss the meaning and application of the principle.

After establishing an understanding of the Golden Rule, use the following scenarios to lead a class discussion. Each scenario provides a situation where a student's behavior will impact other people. Read the example to your class and then seek their feedback on who and how others may be affected in each situation. In each case, ask the students, "How does the Golden Rule apply in this situation? Who and how might others be affected?" Record student responses to summarize each scenario. In each application of the *Golden Compass*, students will be asked, "How does the Golden Rule apply?"

Scenario	How does the Golden Rule apply? Who might be affected? How might others be affected? (Possible responses)
A student bullies a classmate	The classmate could be intimidated and upset by experience Others who observe the behavior may be frustrated Adults could be contacted and need to intervene Bully's parents might be contacted and be upset Others?
A student cheats on a exam	The student cheats himself from really learning the lesson The teacher is mislead by the student who earns a dishonest mark on the exam and misrepresents what he/she learned Fellow students are cheated if the grades are competitive for class standing or further education advancement Parents are mislead in their understanding of their student's learning and behavior Others?
A student serves a neighbor	The neighbor gains the benefit of the student's help The student gains from the neighbor's respect The student's parents are proud of their child The neighborhood is strengthened by the positive interaction Others?

The Golden Rule provides a focus on others to help determine appropriate choices and raise our level of moral reasoning. With the addition of this principle to "do unto others...," we are now ready to introduce the steps for character-based decision making as practiced in the *Golden Compass*.

The *Golden Compass*:
Steps for Character-Based Decisions

The *Golden Compass* decision-making model provides four steps to help students reason through a dilemma. The process guides students to find a good outcome by demonstrating positive character as defined by Aristotle's Golden Mean (page 9). The steps are not complicated. Students in the fifth grade and above readily understand the vocabulary. Review the four steps with your students using the following narrative and refer to a *Golden Compass* poster or make your own poster.

Description of steps

Step One—Stop! Calm down. Everyone recognizes that dilemmas (problems with difficult choices) can affect our emotions. Emotional responses may warn us that we are facing a dilemma. Circumstances that place us in potential conflict with others will increase our emotional anxiety. The first step in using the *Golden Compass* reminds us to calm our emotions so that we can think and take time to understand the dilemma. We will need clear thinking to identify our choices, analyze and resolve our dilemmas. There are many successful strategies that people use to calm themselves. We will identify some of those strategies on the next few pages.

Step Two—Think! Adults and students can strengthen their reasoning skills by practicing to look for choices and options when faced with a dilemma. Practicing the skills of analysis, synthesis and evaluation can be accomplished with the dilemma stories in this activity book. Using our understanding of character developed in the exercises **Personal Character Goals** (page 8) and **Defining the Golden Mean** (page 11) can help us label each choice with a character outcome that would be demonstrated if we were to act on that choice. Also, for each choice, we should ask ourselves, "How does the Golden Rule apply? Who and how will others by affected by my choice." As we practice decision making with The *Golden Compass*, we will continue to strengthen our skills of analysis, synthesis and evaluation.

Step Three—Decide & Act! The decision step requires us to evaluate our options and choose to demonstrate positive character. The decision and action step may require the supporting character trait of courage and self-control for us to demonstrate our choices. In addition to courage, there may be a variety of social skills (such as listening or negotiating) that would help us act on our choices. Developing strong social skills are life-long learning goals that will help us act on our good choices. *[Teachers need to observe and be aware of the social skills that may need to be taught to help students successfully* *implement choices to demonstrate positive character. Resources from Educators for Social Responsibility[14] are terrific curricular support for this important goal.]*

Step Four—Reflect! Our culture rarely gives us the chance to stop and think about our decisions. Students and adults need to make the choice to take time and reflect on our decisions and the results of our actions. This type of reflection step can help guide our decision making in the future. Writing in a journal weekly is a useful strategy to plan regular reflection.

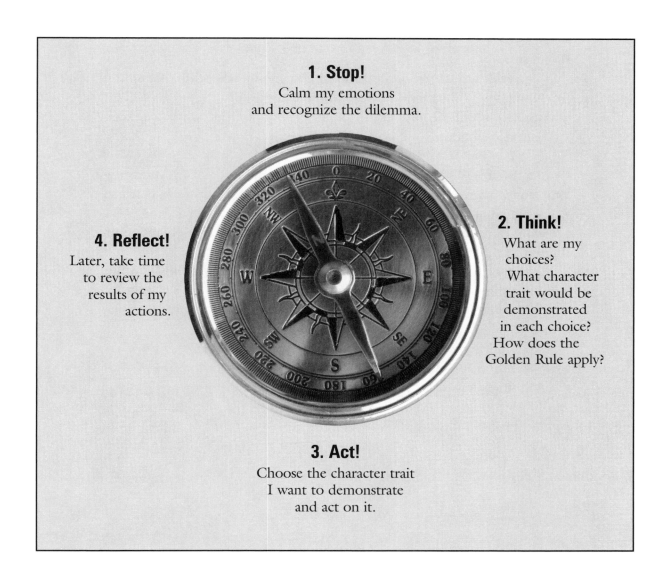

1. Stop!
Calm my emotions
and recognize the dilemma.

2. Think!
What are my
choices?
What character
trait would be
demonstrated
in each choice?
How does the
Golden Rule apply?

3. Act!
Choose the character trait
I want to demonstrate
and act on it.

4. Reflect!
Later, take time
to review the
results of my
actions.

14. Educators for Social Responsibility's website—http://www.esrnational.org/

Step One Strategies: Recognizing and Managing Emotions

The *Golden Compass* requires us to think and good thinking can be blocked by excessive emotions. While emotions can alert us that a dilemma is present, students need to develop their own strategies to calm their emotions and allow themselves the time and place to think.

Use of the *Golden Compass* is a calming strategy in itself. Students will learn by practice that they have options to consider when faced with a dilemma. Students with options can help redirect their emotions by applying the *Golden Compass* process. This act of refocusing is a powerful calming strategy.

Lesson Activity

Objectives:
- Students will identify an emotional continuum and discuss the effects emotions have on their bodies and mind.
- Students will identify and describe calming strategies that help them manage emotions

Use the worksheets (**Recognizing Emotions,** page 27, and **Managing Emotions**, page 28) on the following pages to help students recognize and define 1) what their emotions look like, 2) what they feel like, 3) how emotions can affect their thinking, and 4) strategies to calm their emotions in the face of a dilemma.

Allow time for students to discuss their observations. Help them recognize the physical signs (increased breathing rate, increased heart rate, tense hands, red face...) that should alert them that emotions might be overwhelming their thinking.

After students have identified ways to personally recognize and manage their emotions, provide them opportunities to role play the use of their calming strategies when confronted with a dilemma.

Student Worksheet: Recognizing My Emotions

Name _____

Emotions are part of what makes us human and help us enjoy life. Everyone likes to celebrate birthdays and successful events with friends and family while enjoying the emotions of happiness and belonging in a group. Some of us enjoy a good cry during an emotionally filled movie. Emotions can also get us into trouble. We have all seen the problems that can be caused by someone who allowed the emotions of fear or anger to control them.

Step One for use of the *Golden Compass* is to be able to stop and gain control over emotions. We need to control our emotions to think about choices and solve dilemmas. Recognizing your emotions and how to control them is an important skill. Let's begin with an activity to identify a range of emotions and recognize how they might affect our thinking.

From the following list of emotions, write the emotion below the facial expression that it best describes. For example, the emotion of cheerful is already placed below the facial expression that it matches. More than one emotion may match a facial expression.

Happy, Concerned, Angry, Confused, Scared, Worried, Upset, ~~Cheerful~~, Afraid, Sad

Cheerful

Comprehension/Application: What do you look like and how does your body respond when you are angry? When you are confused? When you are afraid?

Analysis/Evaluation: Has the emotion of anger ever influenced your behavior so that you later regretted what took place?

How does anger affect your thinking?

Reflection: Discuss your observations as a class.

Student Worksheet: Managing My Emotions

Name _____

Emotions can change the way you think. While we don't always need to be cheerful to make good choices, it is often difficult to think well when we are angry or afraid. Most people are able to think more clearly about their choices when their emotions are under control. People have found many ways to control their emotions. Some of those ideas are listed here. Circle the ideas that have worked for you or you think might help in the future.

Count to ten and think about something positive

Talk to someone about the dilemma

Think about a fun place to visit

Go for a walk or jog

Play with a pet

Go window shopping

Draw or paint

Your ideas—

Take slow deep breaths

Be alone and meditate or pray

Be thankful about something

Get a hug

Complete a small chore (wash the dishes)

Write a letter or a poem

Sing

Application/Synthesis: Select one idea to manage your emotions and write or illustrate how you would practice this strategy. Be prepared to share you idea with classmates.

Practicing with the *Golden Compass*

As a practice exercise with the *Golden Compass*, let us return to our dilemma regarding Michael after he discovered his next history test in the school office (we began this story on page 1). Michael is strongly motivated to improve his next test score. Michael should begin with Step One and determine if his emotions are in check and recognize if he does have a dilemma.

Step One: Michael recognizes he is facing a dilemma. He has a conflict between a concern to improve his grades with the availability of the test, and any sense of concern he might have regarding getting caught, his reputation and his sense of honesty. For this case, we will acknowledge that Michael quickly recognizes the dilemma and stops to make sure he does not act out of emotion. Michael calms himself by asking, "What character do I want to demonstrate here?"

Step Two: Michael's next step is to (a) brainstorm his choices, (b) identify what character trait would be demonstrated with each choice and (c) analyze how the Golden Rule would apply to each choice. The following table could summarize his thinking. As an introduction to students, you are encouraged to process these steps with them while recording their responses on the board, a flip chart or overhead.

Choices (Application & Synthesis)	Character Demonstrated (Analysis)	Application of Golden Rule (Analysis & Evaluation)
1. Steal the test and study from it personally.	Immature sense of responsibility, not trustworthy, dishonest, lazy, foolish to risk getting caught	• I would not want this done to me if I were the teacher. • I would not want this done if I was another student without the same benefit from the test. • I would not want this done by my child if I were the parent.
2. Steal the test, study from it personally and copy for friends.	Not trustworthy, dishonest, immature care for others	• I would not want this done to me if I was the teacher. • I would not want this done by my child if I were parent. • I would not want this done if I were a classmate without benefit of the test. • I might not want this dilemma if I were a friend.
3. Leave the test alone and complete his office chore.	Trustworthy, dependable, honest	• No proactive harm done to others. • I would want the test secured by the office staff if I was teacher.
4. Inform someone in the office that the test was lying out.	Trustworthy, dependable, honest, responsible	• Proactive step to help someone else avoid his dilemma, this step would certainly please his teacher and be helpful to other students to avoid the same dilemma.
5. Inform a friend that the test was lying out and suggest he/she take one.	Not trustworthy, manipulative, dishonest	• I would not want this done to me if I was the teacher. • I would not want this done if I was another student without the same benefit from the test. • I would not want to be manipulated if I was another student.

Step Three: Michael's next step is to act on his choice to demonstrate positive character. This step often requires the supporting character traits of courage or self-control. To truly see success as an outcome of this decision, Michael also needs to demonstrate discipline to study on his own and the study skills to know how to study. The study skills and discipline to study would be enabling factors to help Michael choose to act on positive character in this dilemma. Evaluating the existence or absence of these enabling factors can help students and teachers work together to reinforce skills supporting good decisions.

Step Four: After the choice is made and there is time to reflect, Step Four would have Michael think about his decision and compare the results with the consequences that were anticipated at the time of his choice. This step can help reinforce the *Golden Compass* and the value of practicing character-based decision making. If Michael refrained from taking the test, he can celebrate his test results as his own work and not the work that resulted from stealing the test. He can celebrate that his honesty helped him avoid the possible consequences of being caught with the stolen test. Student journals provide a great opportunity to plan for active reflection during the school year.

The *Golden Compass* provides a clear four-step process to guide students with a compass of character to make a good decision. How can this process be taught? Teachers can introduce and practice this life skill in their classrooms. Students need to practice the steps through role modeling and discussion of the workbook dilemmas, and be reminded by adult encouragement, visual aids or written class expectations. Additional practice can be completed with age-appropriate scenarios found in class stories, literature, current events or with circumstances students face at school every day.

New skills and behaviors take time to learn. You are encouraged to provide your students with at least 25 to 30 opportunities to practice the use of the *Golden Compass*. A certificate of completion is included as a copy master (page 90) and students could earn this acknowledgement after successfully completing 25 dilemmas in this workbook. A qualitative survey of observable behaviors is included at the end of this activity book that could be used as a pre- and post-measure of your implementation of the *Golden Compass*.

And finally, celebrate student application of this new skill. Your encouragement and modeling of the process will ultimately be the biggest factor in the successful implementation of the *Golden Compass* in your class or school.

Golden Compass Dilemmas

Golden Compass Dilemma Index

On the Bus (example)
Student Practice Worksheet

Name _____

Background: You witness an older, bigger student being mean to a younger student on the school bus. The bus driver has no idea that this is happening.

The Actors: You, big student, little student, bus driver, others

---

Stop! Are my emotions in control? Do I have a dilemma? (Describe the problem.)

My emotions are under control. I can think this through. Yes, there is a dilemma. I could find myself in a conflict with a bully. I want to help the younger student, but I don't want to get myself in trouble with the bully.

Think!

What are my choices?	What character trait would be demonstrated?	How does the Golden Rule apply?
1. *Say nothing*	*Timid, uncaring*	*Bully likes this idea, but little kid still wants some help*
2. *Distract the bully*	*Caring, creative*	*Bully maybe annoyed and little kid would be grateful*
3. *Tell bully to stop*	*Courage, caring*	*Bully is frustrated with me and little kid would be grateful*
4. *Tell bus driver quietly*	*Caring, responsible*	*Bully is frustrated and little kid would be grateful*

Act! What character trait do I choose to demonstrate? What choice will I make?

_____

_____

What supporting character or skill will I need to act on my choice? Do I need to ask for help?

_____

_____

The Golden Compass for Character-Based Decision Making

Easy Homework

Name _____

Background: Aletha is an excellent student and does her homework each night. You are a good student as well, but you sometimes slack off with homework. Last night was so busy that you were not able to finish your math homework. This morning you notice that Aletha's math paper is sticking out of her book before school. You know you could "borrow" Aletha's paper and copy her homework before class. You could then return her paper right before class begins. No one would have to know.

The Actors: You, Aletha, other students who might witness, math teacher

---

Stop! Are my emotions in control? Do I have a dilemma? (Describe the problem.)

_____

_____

Think!

What are my choices?	What character trait would be demonstrated?	How does the Golden Rule apply?
1.		
2.		
3.		
4.		

Act! What character trait do I choose to demonstrate? What choice will I make?

_____

_____

What supporting character or skill will I need to act on my choice? Do I need to ask for help?

_____

_____

Footnotes

Background: You are under a lot of pressure to turn in an assignment on Monday that requires three sources. You feel you have no time to complete it. You are taking a trip with your family this weekend and there is a favorite show you want to see Sunday night. During some web research, you find several articles that cover the points you want to make in your report; however, the teacher requested you only use one Internet source. You could use the Internet material and fake the information on the sources for the footnotes. How would the teacher know?

The Actors: You, your teacher, fellow students

Stop! Are my emotions in control? Do I have a dilemma? (Describe the problem.)

_____

_____

Think!

What are my choices?	What character trait would be demonstrated?	How does the Golden Rule apply?
1.		
2.		
3.		
4.		

Act! What character trait do I choose to demonstrate? What choice will I make?

_____

_____

What supporting character or skill will I need to act on my choice? Do I need to ask for help?

_____

_____

Thoughtless Assignment

Name _____

Background: You are in a class that you don't enjoy with an assignment to write a paper on a topic you don't care about. You come across an Internet site that allows you to download papers completed by other students. You soon find a paper that would match your current assignment. Its free, its quick and its pretty well written. You could change a few words here and there and make it your own.

The Actors: You, your teacher, fellow classmates

Stop! Are my emotions in control? Do I have a dilemma? (Describe the problem.)

_____

_____

Think!

What are my choices?	What character trait would be demonstrated?	How does the Golden Rule apply?
1.		
2.		
3.		
4.		

Act! What character trait do I choose to demonstrate? What choice will I make?

_____

_____

What supporting character or skill will I need to act on my choice? Do I need to ask for help?

_____

_____

Testing My Character

Name _____

Background: During a quiz, you have forgotten the answer to a question that you have studied. You see a classmate's paper across from you and the answer is filled in. You could read the answer if you tried.

The Actors: You, classmate with answer, other students, your teacher

Stop! Are my emotions in control? Do I have a dilemma? (Describe the problem.)

_____

_____

Think!

What are my choices?	What character trait would be demonstrated?	How does the Golden Rule apply?
1.		
2.		
3.		
4.		

Act! What character trait do I choose to demonstrate? What choice will I make?

_____

_____

What supporting character or skill will I need to act on my choice? Do I need to ask for help?

_____

_____

The Golden Compass for Character-Based Decision Making

The Teacher's Desk Ate It

Name _____

Background: You have forgotten to complete a homework assignment that was due last Friday. You had promised your parents that all of your homework would be turned in this quarter so that they would support you in participating on a town basketball team. The teacher has a reputation for misplacing papers. You can tell your parents that you turned in the assignment and that the teacher lost your work on his messy desk.

The Actors: You, disorganized teacher, your parents

Stop! Are my emotions in control? Do I have a dilemma? (Describe the problem.)

_____

_____

Think!

What are my choices?	What character trait would be demonstrated?	How does the Golden Rule apply?
1.		
2.		
3.		
4.		

Act! What character trait do I choose to demonstrate? What choice will I make?

_____

_____

What supporting character or skill will I need to act on my choice? Do I need to ask for help?

_____

_____

Can You Hear Me Now?

Name _____

Background: The holidays were great this year. You received a new camera phone with lots of free minutes/month. You've learned that classmates are using their phones in text and picture mode to send messages secretly during the school day. During a recent math test a classmate who struggles in the class buzzed you and texted a request for a picture of your test answers.

The Actors: You, phone classmate, your teacher, other classmates, your parents

---

Stop! Are my emotions in control? Do I have a dilemma? (Describe the problem.)

_____

_____

Think!

What are my choices?	What character trait would be demonstrated?	How does the Golden Rule apply?
1.		
2.		
3.		
4.		

Act! What character trait do I choose to demonstrate? What choice will I make?

_____

_____

What supporting character or skill will I need to act on my choice? Do I need to ask for help?

_____

_____

Test Exchange

Name _____

Background: A lot can happen between classes. One thing you have seen in the halls recently is the exchange of information about tests. This has been occurring when a student who completed the exam provides test prep information for those who will take the exam later in the day. This puts you at a real disadvantage if you don't get the information too. Two periods before you are to take a history test, you overhear two students discussing the exam. You want to know what they have to say.

The Actors: You, two other students, your teacher, other classmates

---

Stop! Are my emotions in control? Do I have a dilemma? (Describe the problem.)

_____

_____

Think!

What are my choices?	What character trait would be demonstrated?	How does the Golden Rule apply?
1.		
2.		
3.		
4.		

Act! What character trait do I choose to demonstrate? What choice will I make?

_____

_____

What supporting character or skill will I need to act on my choice? Do I need to ask for help?

_____

_____

Teacher Error

Name _____

Background: An 87, that's great! You relax as you see the grade on your last math test. You didn't think you had done well, so it is a relief to see the score. That will help your average. As the teacher reviews the answers on the test, you recognize that she has misgraded your paper. You add up the points several times and it comes to a 77 each time.

The Actors: You, your teacher, other students

Stop! Are my emotions in control? Do I have a dilemma? (Describe the problem.)

_____

_____

Think!

What are my choices?	What character trait would be demonstrated?	How does the Golden Rule apply?
1.		
2.		
3.		
4.		

Act! What character trait do I choose to demonstrate? What choice will I make?

_____

_____

What supporting character or skill will I need to act on my choice? Do I need to ask for help?

_____

_____

The Golden Compass for Character-Based Decision Making

Integrity What?

Name _____

Background: You have heard that several students and a teacher are beginning an Academic Integrity committee to investigate ways to reduce cheating at school. You agree there is a cheating problem at school. The committee idea is okay, but you cannot imagine how it would work. Is a committee going to change student attitudes about cheating? Today, a friend has asked you to join the committee.

The Actors: You, your friend, others on academic integrity committee, teacher on committee, other students

---

Stop! Are my emotions in control? Do I have a dilemma? (Describe the problem.)

_____

_____

Think!

What are my choices?	What character trait would be demonstrated?	How does the Golden Rule apply?
1.		
2.		
3.		
4.		

Act! What character trait do I choose to demonstrate? What choice will I make?

_____

_____

What supporting character or skill will I need to act on my choice? Do I need to ask for help?

_____

_____

Parent Help

Background: Mom just really likes to help. You are not the best at writing and after you finish a draft, your mom is happy to help you edit. Sometimes she just takes the draft and starts to edit right on the computer. It always turns out better that way. She really knows her writing rules.

The Actors: You, your mom, your teacher, other classmates

Stop! Are my emotions in control? Do I have a dilemma? (Describe the problem.)

_____

_____

Think!

What are my choices?	What character trait would be demonstrated?	How does the Golden Rule apply?
1.		
2.		
3.		
4.		

Act! What character trait do I choose to demonstrate? What choice will I make?

_____

_____

What supporting character or skill will I need to act on my choice? Do I need to ask for help?

_____

_____

Hazy Vision

Name _____

Background: Your school is a pretty safe place, but there are some kids that regularly get pushed around. You see it in the halls, at lunch and in locker rooms. You can see the anger and frustration on the faces of the kids being hazed. They seem like easy targets for this treatment and nobody does anything about it.

The Actors: You, your friends, kids being bullied, bullies, teachers, others?

Stop! Are my emotions in control? Do I have a dilemma? (Describe the problem.)

_____

_____

Think!

What are my choices?	What character trait would be demonstrated?	How does the Golden Rule apply?
1.		
2.		
3.		
4.		

Act! What character trait do I choose to demonstrate? What choice will I make?

_____

_____

What supporting character or skill will I need to act on my choice? Do I need to ask for help?

_____

_____

Enough Is Enough

Name _____

Background: You have a classmate that regularly gets picked on by others. Sometimes you see his papers being damaged or backpack being kicked around by others in the class. It is not just one person treating him poorly. You are not really his friend, but you don't like seeing the mistreatment.

The Actors: You, your classmates, student being mistreated, teachers, others?

Stop! Are my emotions in control? Do I have a dilemma? (Describe the problem.)

_____

_____

Think!

What are my choices?	What character trait would be demonstrated?	How does the Golden Rule apply?
1.		
2.		
3.		
4.		

Act! What character trait do I choose to demonstrate? What choice will I make?

_____

_____

What supporting character or skill will I need to act on my choice? Do I need to ask for help?

_____

_____

The Golden Compass for Character-Based Decision Making

Free Lunch

Name _____

Background: One of your classmates has begun to demand food from other students during lunch. He is bigger and stronger than most of the class and his favorite thing is to take dessert puddings. He doesn't always demand this from the same person. Today he is looking at your friend's lunch tray.

The Actors: You, your friend, your classmates, lunch bully, teachers, others?

Stop! Are my emotions in control? Do I have a dilemma? (Describe the problem.)

_____

_____

Think!

What are my choices?	What character trait would be demonstrated?	How does the Golden Rule apply?
1.		
2.		
3.		
4.		

Act! What character trait do I choose to demonstrate? What choice will I make?

_____

_____

What supporting character or skill will I need to act on my choice? Do I need to ask for help?

_____

_____

2Cool4U

Name _____

Background: One of your friends has always enjoyed the latest clothes and fashions of celebrities. She has become somewhat of a leader of a group of girls with similar interests. Lately, you have seen how her fashion expertise has led her to put down others who are not as well dressed. This morning, she insulted another girl's clothes in front of her and a number of friends. You could see how hurtful this was to the girl that was insulted, but no one said anything in response.

The Actors: You, fashion expert, insulted girl, other students

Stop! Are my emotions in control? Do I have a dilemma? (Describe the problem.)

_____

_____

Think!

What are my choices?	What character trait would be demonstrated?	How does the Golden Rule apply?
1.		
2.		
3.		
4.		

Act! What character trait do I choose to demonstrate? What choice will I make?

_____

_____

What supporting character or skill will I need to act on my choice? Do I need to ask for help?

_____

_____

46   **Dilemmas**   The Golden Compass for Character-Based Decision Making

Go Away!

Name _____

Background: Recess is a great deal of fun, however, you've been seeing some groups during free time exclude classmates from games using excuses like, "The game is almost over." Or, "Each team is full." When the truth is, classmates are being excluded because those who are playing don't like the newcomers or don't think they can play well. You see how this hurts the feelings of those left out.

The Actors: You, your friends, kids being left out, game leaders who keep others out, teachers

---

Stop! Are my emotions in control? Do I have a dilemma? (Describe the problem.)

_____

_____

Think!

What are my choices?	What character trait would be demonstrated?	How does the Golden Rule apply?
1.		
2.		
3.		
4.		

Act! What character trait do I choose to demonstrate? What choice will I make?

_____

_____

What supporting character or skill will I need to act on my choice? Do I need to ask for help?

_____

_____

Is that Really Necessary?

Name _____

Background: Carl is a quiet boy in your class. He gets teased regularly for his lack of athletic ability and his out-of-fashion clothes. You haven't thought much about Carl's circumstance until yesterday when he responded sharply to what seemed like some good natured joking. He angrily warned those teasing him, "Knock it off or you'll regret it." Those who heard him backed off, but made fun of Carl as they walked away. Today, Carl is sitting in front of you when you see a large hunting knife in the open pocket of his backpack. You know that even a butter knife is not allowed at school.

The Actors: You, Carl, other students, teachers, others?

Stop! Are my emotions in control? Do I have a dilemma? (Describe the problem.)

_____

_____

Think!

What are my choices?	What character trait would be demonstrated?	How does the Golden Rule apply?
1.		
2.		
3.		
4.		

Act! What character trait do I choose to demonstrate? What choice will I make?

_____

_____

What supporting character or skill will I need to act on my choice? Do I need to ask for help?

_____

_____

The Golden Compass for Character-Based Decision Making

Are We Having Fun Yet?

Name _____

Background: A classmate that is not very athletic makes a mistake during a game in PE and several students make fun of him/her. It makes you feel very uncomfortable.

The Actors: You, non-athletic classmate, others, PE teacher

Stop! Are my emotions in control? Do I have a dilemma? (Describe the problem.)

_____

_____

Think!

What are my choices?	What character trait would be demonstrated?	How does the Golden Rule apply?
1.		
2.		
3.		
4.		

Act! What character trait do I choose to demonstrate? What choice will I make?

_____

_____

What supporting character or skill will I need to act on my choice? Do I need to ask for help?

_____

_____

Out to Lunch

Name _____

Background: A classmate spills his food tray at lunch and everyone starts laughing. No one offers to help and he becomes very frustrated as he works to clean up the mess. You are watching from your seat about 10 feet away.

The Actors: You, classmate who spills lunch, classmates at your table, others in line

Stop! Are my emotions in control? Do I have a dilemma? (Describe the problem.)

_____

_____

Think!

What are my choices?	What character trait would be demonstrated?	How does the Golden Rule apply?
1.		
2.		
3.		
4.		

Act! What character trait do I choose to demonstrate? What choice will I make?

_____

_____

What supporting character or skill will I need to act on my choice? Do I need to ask for help?

_____

_____

Sticks and Stones

Name _____

Background: It started as just a little teasing, jokes about your ears and your friend Sarah's weight. You thought it was just in fun, but somehow it has become more serious. You see Sarah responding to you with anger and now her remarks are more cutting. The jokes aren't funny anymore.

The Actors: You, Sarah, other students

Stop! Are my emotions in control? Do I have a dilemma? (Describe the problem.)

_____

_____

Think!

What are my choices?	What character trait would be demonstrated?	How does the Golden Rule apply?
1.		
2.		
3.		
4.		

Act! What character trait do I choose to demonstrate? What choice will I make?

_____

_____

What supporting character or skill will I need to act on my choice? Do I need to ask for help?

_____

_____

Just Kidding

Name _____

Background: Jason is the funniest kid in your class. He is able to make up jokes and copy expressions or statements of teachers and classmates in ways that make everyone laugh. His jokes and behavior are funny, but often the humor is insulting to those he copies or tells jokes about. If Jason recognizes his humor makes someone unhappy, he will quickly say, "Just kidding!", but you know he isn't. Lately, Jason has focused his humor on the mannerisms of Laura, one of the girls in the class who isn't very popular. You recognize Laura is very uncomfortable with Jason's behavior.

The Actors: You, Jason, Laura, other classmates, teacher(s)

Stop! Are my emotions in control? Do I have a dilemma? (Describe the problem.)

_____

_____

Think!

What are my choices?	What character trait would be demonstrated?	How does the Golden Rule apply?
1.		
2.		
3.		
4.		

Act! What character trait do I choose to demonstrate? What choice will I make?

_____

_____

What supporting character or skill will I need to act on my choice? Do I need to ask for help?

_____

_____

The Golden Compass for Character-Based Decision Making

Finders Keepers

Name _____

Background: You see a student who you dislike drop a ten-dollar bill out of his backpack and no one else notices.

The Actors: You, another student, others

Stop! Are my emotions in control? Do I have a dilemma? (Describe the problem.)

_____

_____

Think!

What are my choices?	What character trait would be demonstrated?	How does the Golden Rule apply?
1.		
2.		
3.		
4.		

Act! What character trait do I choose to demonstrate? What choice will I make?

_____

_____

What supporting character or skill will I need to act on my choice? Do I need to ask for help?

_____

_____

Quick Reward

Name _____

Background: Your teacher has purchased a number of gift certificates to a local fast food restaurant with her own money. She has kept them in her desk and gives them to students that have shown outstanding effort. A friend took two out of her desk recently and gave one of them to you.

The Actors: You, your friend, your teacher, other students

Stop! Are my emotions in control? Do I have a dilemma? (Describe the problem.)

_____

_____

Think!

What are my choices?	What character trait would be demonstrated?	How does the Golden Rule apply?
1.		
2.		
3.		
4.		

Act! What character trait do I choose to demonstrate? What choice will I make?

_____

_____

What supporting character or skill will I need to act on my choice? Do I need to ask for help?

_____

_____

Gotcha!

Background: Over the last few weeks about four classmates have had money stolen. You are late to class and while walking down an empty hall you turn the corner and see Billy outside your class door pulling something out of a backpack that is lying on the floor. He sees you and quickly walks into class. As you walk towards the door you see the backpack on the floor that belongs to your friend, Anthony. You pick up the backpack and place it on the back counter of the room where Anthony will be sure to see it. Later that day, Anthony reports he has lost his field trip money. You are positive you saw Billy taking something out of Anthony's backpack in the hallway. Billy is a big kid, very athletic and very popular. You do not want to cross him if you can help it.

The Actors: You, Billy, Anthony, other students, teachers, others?

Stop! Are my emotions in control? Do I have a dilemma? (Describe the problem.)

_____

_____

Think!

	What are my choices?	What character trait would be demonstrated?	How does the Golden Rule apply?
1.			
2.			
3.			
4.			

Act! What character trait do I choose to demonstrate? What choice will I make?

_____

_____

What supporting character or skill will I need to act on my choice? Do I need to ask for help?

_____

_____

Forgery

Name _____

Background: You just didn't study for one quiz, got a bad grade and now the teacher wants you to have your parents sign the quiz. The problem is, your folks told you your grades needed to improve if you wanted to participate in the next school social. If they find out about this grade, you'll be grounded for sure. You have a copy of your dad's signature on a permission slip for school. You think you can copy it pretty well.

The Actors: You, your teacher, your parents

Stop! Are my emotions in control? Do I have a dilemma? (Describe the problem.)

_____

_____

Think!

What are my choices?	What character trait would be demonstrated?	How does the Golden Rule apply?
1.		
2.		
3.		
4.		

Act! What character trait do I choose to demonstrate? What choice will I make?

_____

_____

What supporting character or skill will I need to act on my choice? Do I need to ask for help?

_____

_____

Who's Counting Anyway?

Name _____

Background: Thirty hours! Who knew that doing 30 hours of volunteer work would be so difficult? The district recently added 30 hours of community service for graduation and included your class in the requirement. Students need to turn in signed time cards each quarter to get credit from their counselor. You've helped off and on with a local food bank, but you are 10 hours short of the requirement and don't see how you can get them completed. The deadline is next month. You have an earlier time sheet from the food bank with the supervisor's signature. You could copy the form for several weeks and forge the signature for the hours.

The Actors: You, food-bank supervisor, school counselor, others?

Stop! Are my emotions in control? Do I have a dilemma? (Describe the problem.)

_____

_____

Think!

	What are my choices?	What character trait would be demonstrated?	How does the Golden Rule apply?
1.			
2.			
3.			
4.			

Act! What character trait do I choose to demonstrate? What choice will I make?

_____

_____

What supporting character or skill will I need to act on my choice? Do I need to ask for help?

_____

_____

New Kid in School

Name _____

Background: A new student has joined your class and acts very shy and does not smile or act friendly. You tried to start a conversation, but that attempt ended awkwardly.

The Actors: You, new student, others

Stop! Are my emotions in control? Do I have a dilemma? (Describe the problem.)

_____

_____

Think!

What are my choices?	What character trait would be demonstrated?	How does the Golden Rule apply?
1.		
2.		
3.		
4.		

Act! What character trait do I choose to demonstrate? What choice will I make?

_____

_____

What supporting character or skill will I need to act on my choice? Do I need to ask for help?

_____

_____

Family in Need

Name _____

Background: Marc is a classmate whose family is having a very hard time right now. He has not had money for field trips or to participate in some class parties. A big movie is coming out this weekend and a number of friends are planning to go to the theater together. As several of you discuss where you are going to meet before the movie, you see Marc turn and walk away from the group. You know he cannot afford to go.

The Actors: You, Marc, other friends

Stop! Are my emotions in control? Do I have a dilemma? (Describe the problem.)

_____

_____

Think!

What are my choices?	What character trait would be demonstrated?	How does the Golden Rule apply?
1.		
2.		
3.		
4.		

Act! What character trait do I choose to demonstrate? What choice will I make?

_____

_____

What supporting character or skill will I need to act on my choice? Do I need to ask for help?

_____

_____

Friendship Is...

Name _____

Background: Several special education students attend your school and participate in regular subject classes as well as lunch. You have noticed one of the boys is very quiet and shy and often sits alone in the cafeteria. You've smiled and said "hello" a couple times as you walk over to eat lunch with friends, but you barely get a response. As you see him sitting alone across the cafeteria you wonder, "Should I go over, sit down and introduce myself?"

The Actors: You, special needs student, other friends

Stop! Are my emotions in control? Do I have a dilemma? (Describe the problem.)

_____

_____

Think!

What are my choices?	What character trait would be demonstrated?	How does the Golden Rule apply?
1.		
2.		
3.		
4.		

Act! What character trait do I choose to demonstrate? What choice will I make?

_____

_____

What supporting character or skill will I need to act on my choice? Do I need to ask for help?

_____

_____

The Golden Compass for Character-Based Decision Making

She Said What?

Background: At lunch time, you are sitting with friends who are talking about a girl that is absent. People start to make negative comments about her. You are not a close friend with this girl, but you are uncomfortable with people putting her down.

The Actors: You, friends at lunch

Stop! Are my emotions in control? Do I have a dilemma? (Describe the problem.)

_____

_____

Think!

What are my choices?	What character trait would be demonstrated?	How does the Golden Rule apply?
1.		
2.		
3.		
4.		

Act! What character trait do I choose to demonstrate? What choice will I make?

_____

_____

What supporting character or skill will I need to act on my choice? Do I need to ask for help?

_____

_____

Color Blind

Name _____

Background: Your school has students from many racial and ethnic groups. However, you've noticed that groups of friends have been forming that exclude members of other races. Your family has always tried to be color blind when it comes to friends. While you are waiting for the bus after school, one of your classmates makes an insulting comment directed towards a group of students of another race.

The Actors: You, classmates of same race, classmates of different race

Stop! Are my emotions in control? Do I have a dilemma? (Describe the problem.)

_____

_____

Think!

What are my choices?	What character trait would be demonstrated?	How does the Golden Rule apply?
1.		
2.		
3.		
4.		

Act! What character trait do I choose to demonstrate? What choice will I make?

_____

_____

What supporting character or skill will I need to act on my choice? Do I need to ask for help?

_____

_____

Waste Not

Name _____

Background: Your mom always tells you to eat what you purchase from the cafeteria so you will not waste money. Well, she doesn't see what everyone else does during the school lunch. The custodians need to empty the lunchroom trash several times at noon. You see a tremendous amount of wasted food. You wonder if something could be done to reduce the waste or recycle what is being thrown away.

The Actors: You, all students, all adults at school

Stop! Are my emotions in control? Do I have a dilemma? (Describe the problem.)

_____

_____

Think!

What are my choices?	What character trait would be demonstrated?	How does the Golden Rule apply?
1.		
2.		
3.		
4.		

Act! What character trait do I choose to demonstrate? What choice will I make?

_____

_____

What supporting character or skill will I need to act on my choice? Do I need to ask for help?

_____

_____

School Guest

Name _____

Background: You are walking in the school hall just before class begins. The hall is crowded with lots of students. An adult you don't recognize is walking the opposite way, looking a little confused and carrying a lot of stuff. You hear some objects fall on the floor and turn to see the school guest trying to pick up a cardboard tube and a book he just dropped. The bell is just about to ring and you don't want to be late for class.

The Actors: You, school guest, other students

Stop! Are my emotions in control? Do I have a dilemma? (Describe the problem.)

_____

_____

Think!

What are my choices?	What character trait would be demonstrated?	How does the Golden Rule apply?
1.		
2.		
3.		
4.		

Act! What character trait do I choose to demonstrate? What choice will I make?

_____

_____

What supporting character or skill will I need to act on my choice? Do I need to ask for help?

_____

_____

Assembly Speaker

Name _____

Background: What a day! You are on a half-day schedule before a holiday. Your teacher is absent and so is the principal. The speaker for the assembly you are currently attending is not very exciting and students have lost interest. Students are starting to talk and you've seen some paper thrown. Your substitute teacher is standing at the back of the auditorium.

The Actors: You, classmates, other students, substitute, other teachers, speaker, your teacher

Stop! Are my emotions in control? Do I have a dilemma? (Describe the problem.)

_____

_____

Think!

What are my choices?	What character trait would be demonstrated?	How does the Golden Rule apply?
1.		
2.		
3.		
4.		

Act! What character trait do I choose to demonstrate? What choice will I make?

_____

_____

What supporting character or skill will I need to act on my choice? Do I need to ask for help?

_____

_____

Lunch Manners

Name _____

Background: The lunchroom ladies working in the cafeteria have never been very popular. You don't even know their names and they have gotten upset at your class several times for the behavior of just a couple of students. Now you have classmates that have made a game of making lunchtime as unpleasant as possible for the lunchroom workers. Loud noises, dropping food on the floor, knocking over trash cans, it has all been done to irritate the ladies. Some of the pranks have been funny, but you also see a growing frustration in the adults.

The Actors: You, classmates, teachers, lunch ladies, principal

Stop! Are my emotions in control? Do I have a dilemma? (Describe the problem.)

_____

_____

Think!

What are my choices?	What character trait would be demonstrated?	How does the Golden Rule apply?
1.		
2.		
3.		
4.		

Act! What character trait do I choose to demonstrate? What choice will I make?

_____

_____

What supporting character or skill will I need to act on my choice? Do I need to ask for help?

_____

_____

Substitute

Background: Your teacher is absent today and a substitute greets you in the morning. She explains that your regular teacher was not able to leave plans, so she is counting on the class to help her follow the regular routine. Someone suggests a joke to play on the substitute where students switch names. One joke turned into several pranks and now you and a friend are about to hide all the white-board markers. You can see the substitute is getting frustrated.

The Actors: You, friend, other students, substitute, your regular teacher

Stop! Are my emotions in control? Do I have a dilemma? (Describe the problem.)

_____

_____

Think!

	What are my choices?	What character trait would be demonstrated?	How does the Golden Rule apply?
1.			
2.			
3.			
4.			

Act! What character trait do I choose to demonstrate? What choice will I make?

_____

_____

What supporting character or skill will I need to act on my choice? Do I need to ask for help?

_____

_____

Lavatory Break

Name _____

Background: Not again! You are in between classes and some older students are in the back stalls of the lavatory. They are laughing about something, and you can hear scratching on the stall, but you get in and out as fast as you can. Your principal has mentioned the concern about damage occurring in the lavatory. She asked students to help monitor the lavatory and report any problems.

The Actors: You, older students, classmates, teacher, your principal

Stop! Are my emotions in control? Do I have a dilemma? (Describe the problem.)

_____

_____

Think!

What are my choices?	What character trait would be demonstrated?	How does the Golden Rule apply?
1.		
2.		
3.		
4.		

Act! What character trait do I choose to demonstrate? What choice will I make?

_____

_____

What supporting character or skill will I need to act on my choice? Do I need to ask for help?

_____

_____

The Golden Compass for Character-Based Decision Making

Show Me the Money

Name _____

Background: You volunteered to help your club with a carwash as a fundraiser. You have put in a lot more time than most of the other members and your family paid for some supplies to help the event succeed. During the carwash, people have been giving you cash beyond the requested donation for getting their car washed. At the end of the day, you find you have almost $30 in tips in your pocket. You could really use a few dollars for a movie this weekend. You ask yourself, "Is this my money to keep?"

The Actors: You, other club members, club sponsor, your parents

Stop! Are my emotions in control? Do I have a dilemma? (Describe the problem.)

_____

_____

Think!

What are my choices?	What character trait would be demonstrated?	How does the Golden Rule apply?
1.		
2.		
3.		
4.		

Act! What character trait do I choose to demonstrate? What choice will I make?

_____

_____

What supporting character or skill will I need to act on my choice? Do I need to ask for help?

_____

_____

Sweet Deal

Name _____

Background: Your sister's friend has a job at a large discount store. You are with your sister when you meet her friend after work. As you are walking away from the store, she hands you a new CD of an artist you really like. The CD came out of her coat, and as she gives it to you she says, "No need to say thanks, this just comes as part of my work benefits." You don't see a receipt or a store bag for the CD.

The Actors: You, your sister, her friend

Stop! Are my emotions in control? Do I have a dilemma? (Describe the problem.)

_____

_____

Think!

What are my choices?	What character trait would be demonstrated?	How does the Golden Rule apply?
1.		
2.		
3.		
4.		

Act! What character trait do I choose to demonstrate? What choice will I make?

_____

_____

What supporting character or skill will I need to act on my choice? Do I need to ask for help?

_____

_____

　The Golden Compass for Character-Based Decision Making

Teammates

Name _____

Background: You are on a new soccer team in town. Other team members are hazing a classmate that you are not friends with. The hazing is starting to get physical. They don't like his attitude and the coach doesn't seem to know what's going on.

The Actors: You, soccer playing classmate, other team mates, coach

Stop! Are my emotions in control? Do I have a dilemma? (Describe the problem.)

_____

_____

Think!

What are my choices?	What character trait would be demonstrated?	How does the Golden Rule apply?
1.		
2.		
3.		
4.		

Act! What character trait do I choose to demonstrate? What choice will I make?

_____

_____

What supporting character or skill will I need to act on my choice? Do I need to ask for help?

_____

_____

Senior Project

Name _____

Background: You began to notice the changes about a year ago. An elderly man who lives near the school was not out in his yard as often when you walked home. He used to greet you almost every week. This year you haven't seen him at all and his yard is full of leaves and his bushes are over grown.

The Actors: You, other students, senior neighbor

Stop! Are my emotions in control? Do I have a dilemma? (Describe the problem.)

_____

_____

Think!

What are my choices?	What character trait would be demonstrated?	How does the Golden Rule apply?
1.		
2.		
3.		
4.		

Act! What character trait do I choose to demonstrate? What choice will I make?

_____

_____

What supporting character or skill will I need to act on my choice? Do I need to ask for help?

_____

_____

Empty Food Bank

Background: Your service club has chosen to run a canned goods drive for a local food bank. You think it is a great idea until you realize that your best friend is hosting a sleep over for the same weekend you were going to be collecting canned goods.

The Actors: You, other members of service club, best friend, friends invited to sleep over

Stop! Are my emotions in control? Do I have a dilemma? (Describe the problem.)

_____

_____

Think!

What are my choices?	What character trait would be demonstrated?	How does the Golden Rule apply?
1.		
2.		
3.		
4.		

Act! What character trait do I choose to demonstrate? What choice will I make?

_____

_____

What supporting character or skill will I need to act on my choice? Do I need to ask for help?

_____

_____

Deep Discount

Name _____

Background: You and a new friend are shopping in a large department store. Your friend encourages you to join him in stealing some items. You really like this person and want to be friends.

The Actors: You, new friend, people in store

Stop! Are my emotions in control? Do I have a dilemma? (Describe the problem.)

_____

_____

Think!

What are my choices?	What character trait would be demonstrated?	How does the Golden Rule apply?
1.		
2.		
3.		
4.		

Act! What character trait do I choose to demonstrate? What choice will I make?

_____

_____

What supporting character or skill will I need to act on my choice? Do I need to ask for help?

_____

_____

Prank Night

Name _____

Background: It's an autumn Friday night after the game and you are out with friends in the neighborhood. The weather is beautiful, your team won the game and you have a couple hours before you have to be home. Your group decides to pull some harmless pranks on classmates' homes and there are a lot of laughs in the process. Someone suggests a new idea to toss a paint-filled balloon onto an unfriendly neighbor's porch.

The Actors: You, your friends, the neighbor, your parents

Stop! Are my emotions in control? Do I have a dilemma? (Describe the problem.)

_____

_____

Think!

What are my choices?	What character trait would be demonstrated?	How does the Golden Rule apply?
1.		
2.		
3.		
4.		

Act! What character trait do I choose to demonstrate? What choice will I make?

_____

_____

What supporting character or skill will I need to act on my choice? Do I need to ask for help?

_____

_____

Senior Shopping

Name _____

Background: There is an elderly woman who has lived on your street for as long as you can remember. Her husband recently passed away and her children don't live in town. You have watched her carry her groceries home for years. Today, you see her struggling with a walker filled with groceries in the front basket.

The Actors: You, elderly neighbor

Stop! Are my emotions in control? Do I have a dilemma? (Describe the problem.)

_____

_____

Think!

What are my choices?	What character trait would be demonstrated?	How does the Golden Rule apply?
1.		
2.		
3.		
4.		

Act! What character trait do I choose to demonstrate? What choice will I make?

_____

_____

What supporting character or skill will I need to act on my choice? Do I need to ask for help?

_____

_____

The Golden Compass for Character-Based Decision Making

Who's Responsible Here?

Name _____

Background: There is a small park at the end of your street that has fallen into decay. The city has not maintained the benches or the short walking path. The trash receptacle that use to sit near the path has long since disappeared. Litter accumulates along the overgrown shrubbery and the grass areas are either over grown or worn out by children playing. You would like to see the area fixed up.

The Actors: You, neighbors, the City Parks Department

Stop! Are my emotions in control? Do I have a dilemma? (Describe the problem.)

_____

_____

Think!

What are my choices?	What character trait would be demonstrated?	How does the Golden Rule apply?
1.		
2.		
3.		
4.		

Act! What character trait do I choose to demonstrate? What choice will I make?

_____

_____

What supporting character or skill will I need to act on my choice? Do I need to ask for help?

_____

_____

Walking for Hope

Name _____

Background: Your mom's office is sponsoring a team for Walk for Hope, the fundraiser to raise money to fight breast cancer. She has asked you to join her for the walk and collect some sponsors. You agreed to walk with her this Saturday and have collected five sponsors. A friend has just called to say they have extra concert tickets for one of your favorite bands. The concert is Saturday night and four hours away. They are leaving at 11:00 a.m., just when you would be walking with your mom.

The Actors: You, your mom, friends concert tickets, Walk for Hope team

Stop! Are my emotions in control? Do I have a dilemma? (Describe the problem.)

_____

_____

Think!

What are my choices?	What character trait would be demonstrated?	How does the Golden Rule apply?
1.		
2.		
3.		
4.		

Act! What character trait do I choose to demonstrate? What choice will I make?

_____

_____

What supporting character or skill will I need to act on my choice? Do I need to ask for help?

_____

_____

The Golden Compass for Character-Based Decision Making

A Hot Business

Name _____

Background: Everyone knows you are good at burning CDs with a great mix of music. It started out just as a hobby, but as friends heard your mixes at parties, people started to ask you for copies. People are now giving you blank CDs and paying you $3 -$5 to create a new mixed CD for them. You download all the music on your computer and its all free and legal, right?

The Actors: You, friends, and music artists you copy

Stop! Are my emotions in control? Do I have a dilemma? (Describe the problem.)

_____

_____

Think!

What are my choices?	What character trait would be demonstrated?	How does the Golden Rule apply?
1.		
2.		
3.		
4.		

Act! What character trait do I choose to demonstrate? What choice will I make?

_____

_____

What supporting character or skill will I need to act on my choice? Do I need to ask for help?

_____

_____

The Family Car

Name _____

Background: While your parents are away, your brother drives your mother's car without her permission. He doesn't have a license. He doesn't hurt the car, and he even puts gas in the tank on his way home. The one thing he doesn't do is put the keys back exactly where he found them. Later, your mom asks you and your brother if anyone took the keys. Your brother says "not me." He avoids looking at you. Should you cover for him?

The Actors: You, your brother, your parents

Stop! Are my emotions in control? Do I have a dilemma? (Describe the problem.)

_____

_____

Think!

What are my choices?	What character trait would be demonstrated?	How does the Golden Rule apply?
1.		
2.		
3.		
4.		

Act! What character trait do I choose to demonstrate? What choice will I make?

_____

_____

What supporting character or skill will I need to act on my choice? Do I need to ask for help?

_____

_____

At High Speed

Name _____

Background: While surfing the web on a computer at a friend's house, she logged-on to a pornographic website. You have promised your parents to stay out of pornographic websites.

The Actors: You, your friend, your parents

Stop! Are my emotions in control? Do I have a dilemma? (Describe the problem.)

_____

_____

Think!

What are my choices?	What character trait would be demonstrated?	How does the Golden Rule apply?
1.		
2.		
3.		
4.		

Act! What character trait do I choose to demonstrate? What choice will I make?

_____

_____

What supporting character or skill will I need to act on my choice? Do I need to ask for help?

_____

_____

Up in Smoke

Name _____

Background: People are changing at school. One of your old friends has started to change his attitude toward school and activities. You still get along, but he has dropped out of the teams you had both participated in. Today, he invited you to join him after school to hang out. When you show up, you see that he and some others are smoking. You've never smoked before and never thought you'd start. You are offered a cigarette.

The Actors: You, your old friend, other kids

Stop! Are my emotions in control? Do I have a dilemma? (Describe the problem.)

_____

_____

Think!

What are my choices?	What character trait would be demonstrated?	How does the Golden Rule apply?
1.		
2.		
3.		
4.		

Act! What character trait do I choose to demonstrate? What choice will I make?

_____

_____

What supporting character or skill will I need to act on my choice? Do I need to ask for help?

_____

_____

I Dare You

Background: First it was with skateboards and then it was bikes, Matt was always up to some challenge. The steepest hill, the biggest jump, the fastest ride were all things that attracted Matt and then he would challenge his friends, "I dare you." You and some others are over at Matt's home and he is showing you how he gets a buzz by inhaling some of his dad's modeling glue. You know what's coming next.

The Actors: You, Matt, other friends

Stop! Are my emotions in control? Do I have a dilemma? (Describe the problem.)

_____

_____

Think!

What are my choices?	What character trait would be demonstrated?	How does the Golden Rule apply?
1.		
2.		
3.		
4.		

Act! What character trait do I choose to demonstrate? What choice will I make?

_____

_____

What supporting character or skill will I need to act on my choice? Do I need to ask for help?

_____

_____

PG to R

Background: Your folks are really strict when it comes to the movies they let you see. They just approved and paid for you to see a PG film after you had argued to see another movie with an R rating. You and two friends have just bought your tickets at a large Cineplex with eight movies showing this afternoon. As you hand over your ticket to enter, one of your friends suggests you all go into the bathroom and then exit and go to the R-rated movie you all wanted to see in the first place.

The Actors: You, two friends, your parents

Stop! Are my emotions in control? Do I have a dilemma? (Describe the problem.)

_____

_____

Think!

What are my choices?	What character trait would be demonstrated?	How does the Golden Rule apply?
1.		
2.		
3.		
4.		

Act! What character trait do I choose to demonstrate? What choice will I make?

_____

_____

What supporting character or skill will I need to act on my choice? Do I need to ask for help?

_____

_____

Senior Center

Name _____

Background: Your granddad has recently been admitted to a nursing home. You used to enjoy visiting him at his apartment, but now it is very uncomfortable for you to go see him. You don't like the smell at the nursing home, the other residents try to reach out and touch you and your granddad doesn't speak as clearly anymore. Your mom invites you to go visit Granddad on Saturday. Your friends have invited you to go to the mall.

The Actors: You, your parents, your granddad, friends

Stop! Are my emotions in control? Do I have a dilemma? (Describe the problem.)

_____

_____

Think!

What are my choices?	What character trait would be demonstrated?	How does the Golden Rule apply?
1.		
2.		
3.		
4.		

Act! What character trait do I choose to demonstrate? What choice will I make?

_____

_____

What supporting character or skill will I need to act on my choice? Do I need to ask for help?

_____

_____

Is that Thing Loaded?

Name _____

Background: After school, a friend invited you over and you discovered no one else was at home. He wanted to show you something cool and brings out his dad's revolver. He begins to play as if he were shooting a robber coming into the home and swings the gun pointing it all around the room.

The Actors: You, your friend

Stop! Are my emotions in control? Do I have a dilemma? (Describe the problem.)

_____

_____

Think!

What are my choices?	What character trait would be demonstrated?	How does the Golden Rule apply?
1.		
2.		
3.		
4.		

Act! What character trait do I choose to demonstrate? What choice will I make?

_____

_____

What supporting character or skill will I need to act on my choice? Do I need to ask for help?

_____

_____

Chore Time

Name _____

Background: You've been doing chores around the home since you were a little kid. You have a regular list you are responsible for each week and your mom rarely checks to see if you've completed them anymore. A friend has called and asked you to come over and join her family to go to a movie. They are leaving in 15 minutes. Your mom says "okay" as long as your chores are done. It takes you at least 30 minutes to complete your chores and you haven't started.

The Actors: You, your friends, your mom

Stop! Are my emotions in control? Do I have a dilemma? (Describe the problem.)

_____

_____

Think!

What are my choices?	What character trait would be demonstrated?	How does the Golden Rule apply?
1.		
2.		
3.		
4.		

Act! What character trait do I choose to demonstrate? What choice will I make?

_____

_____

What supporting character or skill will I need to act on my choice? Do I need to ask for help?

_____

_____

Just One Drink

Name _____

Background: Charlie is a leader in and out of school. You and a group of friends have gotten together at Charlie's house while his folks are away. Someone has opened his parents' liquor cabinet and has started pouring drinks. It has become a challenge, "Hey, try just one." Several of your friends are sampling drinks from different bottles. You've just been watching until the challenge comes straight to you.

The Actors: You, Charlie, your friends

Stop! Are my emotions in control? Do I have a dilemma? (Describe the problem.)

_____

_____

Think!

What are my choices?	What character trait would be demonstrated?	How does the Golden Rule apply?
1.		
2.		
3.		
4.		

Act! What character trait do I choose to demonstrate? What choice will I make?

_____

_____

What supporting character or skill will I need to act on my choice? Do I need to ask for help?

_____

_____

Cranking Away

Name _____

Background: You and a friend are at home when you get a crank call from one of your buddies. You identify him immediately and he hangs up. But now you get "cranking" too. You have an unlisted number and don't think you can be identified. You've been calling friends and had some good laughs but then start dialing random numbers. An elderly woman answers the call and appears quite upset before you hung up.

The Actors: You, your friend, people you called, elderly woman

---

Stop! Are my emotions in control? Do I have a dilemma? (Describe the problem.)

_____

_____

Think!

What are my choices?	What character trait would be demonstrated?	How does the Golden Rule apply?
1.		
2.		
3.		
4.		

Act! What character trait do I choose to demonstrate? What choice will I make?

_____

_____

What supporting character or skill will I need to act on my choice? Do I need to ask for help?

_____

_____

THE GOLDEN COMPASS

Golden Compass

Certificate of Training Completion

is recognized for completing 25 dilemmas using the *Golden Compass*. You are commended for applying positive character to understand, analyze, evaluate and choose positive options to solve dilemmas. You are encouraged to apply your values with the *Golden Compass* in all your future decision making.

_____
Teacher

_____
Date

Supporting Resources

The following student survey may be used to estimate your students' level of moral reasoning from Stages One to Five.

As one begins to work with students to teach character-based decision making, it is useful to make a simple, qualitative "audit" of their current stage of moral reasoning. Assign the students to anonymously and individually complete the worksheet **What Motivates Me**.

This worksheet does not have any tested psychometric properties. Responses from the exercise are only for qualitative purposes to estimate the stage of moral reasoning held by students in your class. The worksheet should remain anonymous and can be scored by the students before they hand them back to you.

Scores from this worksheet can provide a rough estimate of student's moral reasoning for Stages 1-5. No items or statements are included to identify Stage 6. Kohlberg was known to joke that he was the only person who he recognized to achieve Stage 6. A goal for completing this exercise should be to understand how many students might benefit from experiences to bump up to Stage Three. Stage Three is the first stage where individuals take into consideration the concerns of others (close to them) as highlighted in the Golden Rule.

Administering *What Motivates Me*

1. Students should work independently and in a quiet environment
2. Students should work quickly and respond to each item (statement) with their first impression
3. Students should check only one box for each item

Scoring *What Motivates Me*

Students may score their own completed worksheet.

1. Assign points (see scoring key below) *only* to boxes checked in **Sounds Like Me** column.
2. Cross out (drop) the four lowest scores and add up the balance of the points assigned in **Sounds Like Me** column.

3. Divide the total number of points by the number of items selected (remembering to drop four scores) in **Sounds Like Me** column. **Example:** Sum of 28 points for 8 items in Sounds Like Me 28 / 8 = 3.5

4. Round division to tenths and compare answer (a number between 1 and 5) to Kohlberg's Moral Development Stages descriptions on page 12.

Scoring Key

Item 1=3points	Item 8=5 points	Item 15=4 points
Item 2=4 points	Item 9=1 point	Item 16=1 point
Item 3=2 points	Item 10=5 points	Item 17=2 points
Item 4=1 point	Item 11=3 points	Item 18=3 points
Item 5=5 points,	Item 12=4 points	Item 19=3 points
Item 6=1 point	Item 13=5 points	Item 20=2 points
Item 7=4 points	Item 14=2 points	

What Motivates Me

Class/Subject _____ Date
(Do not write your name on this sheet.)

After each statement, make a check ✔ in the column that best describe you (Sounds Like Me) or (Doesn't Sound Like Me). Work independently and quickly respond with your first impression. You must choose only one box per statement. Please do not cross out any selections. Your teacher will help you score the results.

Item	Statement	Sounds Like Me	Doesn't Sound Like Me
1	I really enjoy helping my family with their projects.		
2	I support the rules here to help us stay safe.		
3	If there is no extra reward, why should I do this?		
4	I avoid trouble, because I hate getting caught.		
5	I think it is best to help the greatest number of people even if a few are left out.		
6	What is most important to me is to get my way and have fun.		
7	If that is what the rule says, that is what I am going to obey.		
8	If resources are limited, I think the majority should get the most help.		
9	Avoiding getting caught is a big deal to me.		
10	It is OK if some people need to sacrifice for the best interest of the group.		
11	I would never want to disappoint my family.		
12	It is important to me to obey the rules so that everything stays in order.		
13	Sometimes a few people don't get their way for the benefit of the group.		
14	Do I get extra pizza if I do this?		
15	I don't care if it is hard; I am going to follow the rules.		
16	My main goal is to seek the most fun for myself.		
17	Don't ask me to help if I don't get what I want.		
18	I respect my teachers and work hard for them.		
19	I would never do anything to hurt my parents.		
20	If there is something in it for me, I will help.		
	Total points		
	(Listen for directions to calculate final score) **Final Score**		

Capturing a View of Choices

We have affirmed that one definition of character is the visible demonstration of behavior following the choices that people make. The sum of these choices will define the character of individuals and groups. Measuring the character of a class or school is truly a challenging task; however, qualitative results from surveys and questionnaires can point us in directions to make progress to create a positive school climate.

The following survey is one qualitative instrument to help capture a measure of the character choices of your students. Complete the survey prior to implementing your *Golden Compass* program and have your students retake the survey after they have completed over 25 exercises from this activity book over a period of at least 3 months. Compare your results between the two administrations of the survey and evaluate for shifts in responses in the categories your school or class is focused upon. The items in this survey qualitatively measure student responses to themes related to (1) academic integrity, (2) respect, (3) honesty, (4) empathy, and (5) responsibility.

Capturing a View of Choices

Date _____

Please do not place your name on the paper.

Class _____ School _____ Boy   Girl

(Circle Gender)

Working by yourself, place a mark with your first impression in the column that best describes your opinion about the following behaviors you may see at your school.

SA = Strongly Agree   **A = Agree**   **D = Disagree**   **SD = Strongly Disagree**

		SA	A	D	SD
1.	Students complete homework and tests honestly.				
2.	Students at this school are generally irresponsible.				
3.	Students bully other students here.				
4.	I trust my classmates not to mess with my stuff.				
5.	Most students don't care about the needs of others.				
6.	I often see students step up to do the right thing.				
7.	Students cite their sources properly on written assignments.				
8.	Students show respect for one another and teachers.				
9.	I see students go out of their way to help others.				
10.	Students can not be trusted to make good decisions.				
11.	Students cheat on homework and tests.				
12.	Students don't tolerate mean teasing or exclusive behavior here.				
13.	Stealing is a problem at this school.				
14.	Our students quickly respond to help others in need.				
15.	I am proud of the responsibility shown by our students.				
16.	Students plagiarize material off the internet or other sources.				
17.	Students are insulting to teachers and other adults.				
18.	I don't trust many students.				
19.	It's disappointing to see how students respond to people who need help.				
20.	People respect the property of others here.				

Summary of Capturing a View of Choices

Record summary of responses for first survey, retake and differences in the columns below.

Date of first survey _____   Classes participating_____

Total number of students _____   # Girls _____   # Boys _____

Date of second survey_____   Classes participating_____

Total number of students _____   # Girls _____   # Boys _____

SA = Strongly Agree   **A = Agree**   **D = Disagree**   **SD = Strongly Disagree**

Choices you see	SA1	SA2	Diff SA2-SA1=	A1	A2	Diff A2-A1=	D1	D2	Diff D2-D1=	SD1	SD2	Diff SD2-SD1=
1. Students complete homework and tests honestly.												
2. Students at this school are generally irresponsible.												
3. Students bully other students here.												
4. I trust my classmates not to mess with my stuff.												
5. Most students don't care about the needs of others.												
6. I often see students step up to do the right thing.												
7. Students cite their sources properly on written assignments.												
8. Students show respect for one another and teachers.												
9. I see students go out of their way to help others.												
10. Students can not be trusted to make good decisions.												
11. Students cheat on homework and tests.												
12. Students don't tolerate mean teasing or exclusive behavior here.												

Choices you see	SA1	SA2	Diff SA2-SA1=	A1	A2	Diff A2-A1=	D1	D2	Diff D2-D1=	SD1	SD2	Diff SD2-SD1=
13. Stealing is a problem at this school.												
14. Our students quickly respond to help others in need.												
15. I am proud of the responsibility shown by our students.												
16. Students plagiarize material off the internet or other sources.												
17. Students are insulting to teachers and other adults.												
18. I don't trust many students.												
19. It's disappointing to see how students respond to people who need help.												
20. People respect the property of others here.												

Summary of Capturing a View of Choices

Date _____

Record the difference scores (Diff) for each item and note the goal of increasing scores for strongly agree/agree correspond with positively written items and goal to seek increases in strongly disagree/disagree are for negatively written items.

Analyze your results to track the trends of your student responses.

Seeking Increase	Item #	Item Themes	Score Differences:	SA	A	D	SD
		Academic Integrity					
SA, A	1	Students complete homework and tests honestly.					
SA, A	7	Students cite their sources properly on written assignments.					
SD, D	11	Students cheat on homework and tests.					
SD, D	16	Students plagiarize material off the internet or other sources.					
		Respect					
SA, A	8	Students show respect for one another and teachers.					
SA, A	12	Students don't tolerate mean teasing or exclusive behavior here.					
SD, D	17	Students are insulting to teachers and other adults.					
SD, D	3	Students bully other students here.					
		Honesty					
SA, A	4	I trust my classmates not to mess with my stuff.					
SA, A	20	People respect the property of others here.					
SD, D	13	Stealing is a problem at this school.					
SD, D	18	I don't trust many students.					
		Empathy					
SA, A	9	I see students go out of their way to help others.					
SA, A	14	Our students quickly respond to help others in need.					
SD, D	5	Most students don't care about the needs of others.					
SD, D	19	It's disappointing to see how students respond to people who need help.					
		Responsibility					
SA, A	6	I often see students step up to do the right thing.					
SA, A	15	I am proud of the responsibility shown by our students.					
SD, D	10	Students can not be trusted to make good decisions.					
SD, D	2	Students at this school are generally irresponsible.					